Andrew Brodie Basics

LET'S DO MENTAL MATHS

FOR AGES 8-9

with over **100** reward stickers

- Over 800 practice questions
- Regular progress tests
- Extra tips and brain booster questions

First published 2013 by Bloomsbury Publishing plc
50 Bedford Square, London, WC1B 3DP
www.bloomsbury.com

ISBN 978-1-4081-8337-3

Copyright © 2013 Bloomsbury Publishing plc
Written by Andrew Brodie
Design by Marcus Duck
Cover and inside illustrations of Digit the Dog and Andrew Brodie © Nikalas Catlow

10 9 8 7 6 5 4 3 2 1

A CIP record for this publication is available from the British Library.

Printed in China by Leo Paper Products

This book is produced using paper that is made from wood grown in managed, sustainable forests. It is natural, renewable and recyclable. The logging and manufacturing processes conform to the environmental regulations of the country of origin.

To see our full range of titles visit www.bloomsbury.com

BLOOMSBURY

Notes for parents

What's in this book

This is the fourth book in an exciting new series of *Andrew Brodie Basics: Let's Do Mental Maths* books. Each book contains more than 800 mental maths questions specially devised to boost children's confidence by providing plenty of practice in all the key aspects of the National Curriculum:

• Number and place value
• Addition and subtraction
• Multiplication and division
• Fractions
• Measures
• Geometry

The structure of each test follows the same pattern but the questions become gradually more difficult as the book progresses. You will notice that some questions are repeated to help your child learn and then revise vital facts such as identifying shapes: squares, triangles, rectangles and circles. Taking the time to discuss the questions with your child and helping to explain anything they find difficult will produce the best results. Answers to all the questions are provided at the back of the book.

How you can help

To begin with your child might find the tests quite tricky but as they work their way through the book and become more familiar with the different types of question their confidence will grow. At the end of every five tests there is a Progress Test which will help you and your child to review some of the key concepts and will also highlight anything they haven't understood so far. Always provide lots of encouragement and explain that they should learn from their mistakes rather than be disheartened.

Children gain confidence by learning facts that they can use in their work at school. Help your child by displaying posters on their bedroom wall, showing facts such as the times tables, days of the week and months of the year. Talk about these facts with your child and other topics that children find difficult such as fractions.

Explain that the circle is cut into four pieces so we are dealing with quarters; 1 of these is shaded so the fraction shaded is one quarter. We write one quarter like this:

$$\frac{1}{4}$$

Some children have difficulty with the concept of a fraction of a set of objects.

The fraction shown here is, of course, $\frac{4}{8}$ and some children will quickly see that this is the same as $\frac{1}{2}$. Other children simply won't get it! If this is the case it's best to encourage them to identify the fraction correctly as $\frac{4}{8}$ and return to discussing it later, perhaps as long as 6 months or even a year later. Concepts that proved tricky to begin with can suddenly fall into place. It's most important that children don't feel pressurized into tackling questions that are beyond their conceptual understanding. With patience, praise and encouragement they will grasp concepts at an appropriate stage in their development and are likely then to gallop ahead.

Digit the Dog and Brain Boosters

Look out for useful tips from Digit the Dog who provides little snippets of mathematical information that your child needs to know or quick questions to get them thinking!

Brodie's Brain Boosters feature short mathematical problems, which can be solved by working logically. Some of these may look very straightforward but the thinking processes that your child will need to apply are important skills to practise, ready for more challenging work later. Understanding the wording of questions is a crucial aspect of problem solving so ensure that your child reads each question carefully – give some help with the vocabulary if necessary.

With lots of practice and encouragement your child will see their score improve day by day!

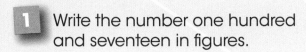 

Score:

1. Write the number one hundred and seventeen in figures.

2. What number is halfway between sixteen and twenty?

3. Put these numbers in order, starting with the smallest:
36 603 360 63 630 306

4. Round 387 to the nearest ten.

5. What number is 100 less than 345?

6. $46 + 7 =$

7. Decrease 82 by 35.

8. What is the difference between 90 and 17?

9. Add 47 to 53.

10. Double 2.

11. $6 \times 4 =$

12. What is 7 multiplied by 4?

13. How much do I spend when I buy 4 pencils costing 22p each?

14. What fraction of the circle is shaded?

15. Simplify the fraction $\frac{2}{4}$

16. Write this fraction as a decimal $\frac{1}{2}$

17. How many days are there in one year (not a leap year)?

18. How many metres are there in a kilometre?

19. How many minutes are there in an hour?

20. $25cm + 15cm =$

Brodie's Brain Booster

My workbench is 2 metres long. How long is that in centimetres?

3

TEST 2

Score: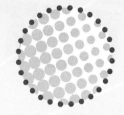

1. Write the number eight hundred and four in figures.

2. What number is halfway between six and ten?

3. Put these numbers in order, starting with the smallest:
105 51 510 15 501 150

4. Round 247 to the nearest ten.

5. What number is 100 less than 598?

6. Add 6 to 38.

7. 75 take away 20.

8. 65 + 18 =

9. 81 subtract 47.

10. Multiply 2 by 7.

11. Double 5 =

12. 5 x 3 =

13. What is 6 multiplied by 2?

14. What fraction of the circle is shaded?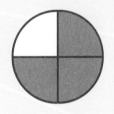

15. Simplify the fraction $\frac{2}{8}$

16. Write this fraction as a decimal $\frac{1}{4}$

17. How many months are there in one year?

18. How many metres are there in half a kilometre?

19. How many minutes are there in half an hour?

20. 28cm + 22cm =

Digit says...
Remember that there are 1000 metres in a kilometre.

TEST 3

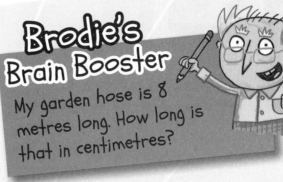

Brodie's Brain Booster

My garden hose is 8 metres long. How long is that in centimetres?

1 Write the number two hundred and fifty-seven in figures.

2 What number is halfway between twenty and thirty?

3 Put these numbers in order, starting with the smallest:
216 21 61 612 126 621

4 Round 591 to the nearest ten.

5 What number is 100 less than 624?

6 36 plus 12 =

7 62 minus 47 =

8 What is the total of 67 and 23?

9 95 – 33 =

10 Multiply 4 by 5.

11 How much do I spend when I buy 3 pencils costing 24p each?

12 Double 3 =

13 9 x 5 =

14 What fraction of the circle is shaded?

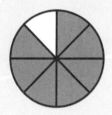

15 Simplify the fraction $\frac{6}{8}$

16 Write this fraction as a decimal $\frac{1}{4}$

17 How many days are there in a leap year?

18 How many metres are there in a quarter of a kilometre?

19 How many minutes are there in a quarter of an hour?

20 36cm + 14cm =

TEST 4

Digit says...

My walk yesterday was 8km long so I must have walked 8000m. It's not surprising that my human was exhausted!

1 Write the number nine hundred and two in figures.

2 What number is halfway between thirty and forty?

3 Put these numbers in order, starting with the smallest:
804 408 48 84 480 840

4 Round 856 to the nearest ten.

5 What number is 100 less than 739?

6 What is the total of 18 and 23?

7 50 subtract 26.

8 29 plus 58 =

9 95 minus 55 =

10 What is 8 multiplied by 3?

11 Multiply 6 by 4.

12 How much do I spend when I buy 2 pencils costing 98p each?

13 Double 4 =

14 What fraction of the circle is shaded?

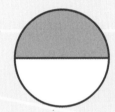

15 Simplify the fraction $\frac{3}{6}$

16 Write this fraction as a decimal $\frac{1}{4}$

17 What is the first month of the year?

18 How many metres are there in three quarters of a kilometre?

19 How many minutes are there in three quarters of an hour?

20 42cm + 18cm =

TEST 5

1 Write the number one hundred and eleven in figures.

2 What number is halfway between fifteen and nineteen?

3 Put these numbers in order, starting with the smallest:
697 69 97 79 796 679

4 Round 342 to the nearest ten.

5 What number is 100 less than 555?

6 Increase 49 by 26.

7 62 – 28 =

8 58p + 22p =

9 Decrease 100 by 46.

10 7 x 3 =

11 What is 9 multiplied by 4?

12 Multiply 5 by 7.

13 How much do I spend when I buy 5 pencils costing 25p each?

14 What fraction of the circle is shaded?

15 Simplify the fraction $\frac{2}{6}$

16 Write this fraction as a decimal $\frac{3}{4}$

17 What is the second month of the year?

18 How many metres are there in two kilometres?

19 How many minutes are there in two hours?

20 73cm + 17cm =

Brodie's Brain Booster

My car is $4\frac{1}{2}$ metres long. How long is that in centimetres?

7

Addition

1 36 + 22 =

2 80 + 40 =

Subtraction

3 80 − 36 =

4 100 − 44 =

Multiplication

5 Double 6 =

6 8 x 5 =

Division

7 12 ÷ 2 =

8 20 ÷ 4 =

Money

9 How much do I spend when I buy 5 pencils costing 15p each?

10 25p + 46p =

Fractions

11 What fraction of the circle is shaded?

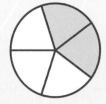

12 Write this fraction as a decimal $\frac{1}{2}$

Number knowledge

13 Write the number nine hundred and ninety-nine in figures.

14 Put these numbers in order, starting with the smallest:
185 581 851 518 158 815

Measurement

15 42cm + 18cm =

16 How many metres are there in three kilometres?

Time

17 How many minutes are there in an hour?

18 What is the third month of the year?

Number problems

19 What number is halfway between eight and twelve?

20 What is one hundred more than eighty-two?

Score chart

Test	1	2	3	4	5	Progress
Score						

8

TEST 6

Score:

1 Write the number seven hundred and seventy-seven in figures.

2 What number is halfway between 20 and 24?

3 Put these numbers in order, starting with the smallest: 907 709 97 790 79 970

4 Round 994 to the nearest ten.

5 What number is 100 less than 942?

6 Increase 98 by 16.

7 84 take away 39 =

8 What is the next number in this sequence? 27, 29, 31, 33, …

9 I think of a number. I add 14. My answer is 31. What number did I first think of?

10 What is 6 multiplied by 5?

11 Multiply 3 by 9.

12 How much do I spend when I buy 4 pencils costing 58p each?

13 Double 7 =

14 What fraction of the circle is shaded?

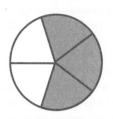

15 Simplify the fraction $\frac{4}{6}$

16 Write this fraction as a decimal $\frac{1}{10}$

17 What is the fourth month of the year?

18 Find the perimeter of a rectangle with sides of 4cm and 6cm.

6cm

4cm

19 I get up at quarter past seven in the morning. Show the time in digital format.

20 1m – 46cm =

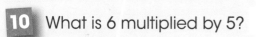

Digit says...

Remember that there are 1000 millimetres in a metre.

TEST 7

1 Write the number one thousand two hundred and fourteen in figures.

2 What number is halfway between 30 and 36?

3 Put these numbers in order, starting with the smallest:
118 811 81 18 181 8

4 Round 127 to the nearest ten.

5 What number is 100 less than 907?

6 Add 68 to 59.

7 What is the difference between 12 and 40?

8 What is the next number in this sequence? 5, 10, 15, 20, ...

9 I think of a number. I add 21. My answer is 40. What number did I first think of?

10 9 × 4 =

11 What is 6 multiplied by 6?

12 Multiply 4 by 8.

13 How much do I spend when I buy 4 pencils costing 75p each?

14 What fraction of the circle is shaded?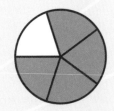

15 Simplify the fraction $\frac{2}{4}$

16 Write this fraction as a decimal $\frac{2}{10}$

17 What is the fifth month of the year?

18 Find the perimeter of a rectangle with sides of 3cm and 6cm.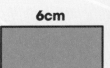
6cm
3cm

19 I have breakfast at half past seven in the morning. Show the time in digital format.

20 1m – 38cm =

Brodie's Brain Booster

Digit's front legs are each a quarter of a metre long. How many centimetres are there in a quarter of a metre?

TEST 8

Digit says...

My tail is $\frac{1}{2}$m long, which is 500mm. That's impressive!

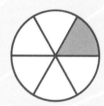

1 Write the number seven thousand three hundred and twenty-seven in figures.

2 What number is halfway between 40 and 50?

3 Put these numbers in order, starting with the smallest:
345 354 543 453 534 435

4 Round 654 to the nearest ten.

5 What number is 100 more than 267?

6 75 plus 50 =

7 71 – 33 =

8 What is the next number in this sequence? 32, 34, 36, 38, …

9 I think of a number. I add 17. My answer is 34. What number did I first think of?

10 Double 8 =

11 5 x 4 =

12 What is 9 multiplied by 5?

13 Multiply 6 by 3.

14 What fraction of the circle is shaded?

15 Simplify the fraction $\frac{2}{10}$

16 Write this fraction as a decimal $\frac{3}{10}$

17 What is the sixth month of the year?

18 Find the perimeter of a rectangle with sides of 2cm and 6cm.

6cm

2cm

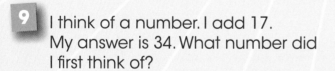

19 I walk to school at 8 o'clock in the morning. Show the time in digital format.

20 1m – 49cm =

TEST 9

Brodie's Brain Booster

How many centimetres are there in three quarters of a metre?

1 Write the number five thousand five hundred and twenty in figures.

2 What number is halfway between 31 and 37?

3 Put these numbers in order, starting with the smallest:
406 64 604 640 46 460

4 Round 779 to the nearest ten.

5 What number is 100 more than 518?

6 What is the total of 88 and 23?

7 90 subtract 44 =

8 What is the next number in this sequence? 39, 42, 45, 48, …

9 I think of a number. I add 18. My answer is 30. What number did I first think of?

10 How much do I spend when I buy 4 pencils costing 82p each?

11 Double 9 =

12 7 x 5 =

13 What is 6 multiplied by 4?

14 What fraction of the circle is shaded?

15 Simplify the fraction $\frac{4}{10}$

16 Write this fraction as a decimal $\frac{4}{10}$

17 What is the seventh month of the year?

18 Find the perimeter of a rectangle with sides of 5cm and 6cm.

6cm

5cm

19 The caretaker opens my school at 7 o'clock in the morning. Show the time in digital format.

20 1m – 87cm =

12

TEST 10

Score:

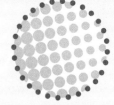

1 Write the numbe three thousand and forty-six in figures.

2 What number is halfway between 43 and 49?

3 Put these numbers in order, starting with the smallest:
73 137 17 317 173 37

4 Round 445 to the nearest ten.

5 What number is 100 more than 832?

6 Increase 92 by 26.

7 81 minus 25 =

8 What is the next number in this sequence? 61, 66, 71, 76, …

9 I think of a number. I add 24. My answer is 40. What number did I first think of?

10 Multiply 5 by 9.

11 How much do I spend when I buy 4 pencils costing 99p each?

12 Double 11 =

13 6 x 6 =

14 What fraction of the circle is shaded?

15 Simplify the fraction $\frac{6}{10}$

16 Write this fraction as a decimal $\frac{5}{10}$

17 What is the eighth month of the year?

18 Find the perimeter of a rectangle with sides of 4cm and 5cm.

5cm

4cm

19 My alarm goes off at ten past seven in the morning. Show the time in digital format.

20 1m – 64cm =

Digit says...

When rounding a number that ends in 10 always remember to round it up

13

Addition

1 Increase 48 by 26.

2 What is the total of 16 and 18?

Subtraction

3 72 minus 24 =

4 What is the difference between 60 and 12?

Multiplication

5 What is 8 multiplied by 2?

6 Double 16 =

Division

7 $12 \div 4 =$

8 $15 \div 3 =$

Money

9 How much do I spend when I buy 4 pencils costing 19p each?

10 What is my change from £1 when I spend 24p?

Fractions

11 What fraction of the circle is shaded?

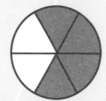

12 Write this fraction as a decimal $\frac{6}{10}$

Number knowledge

13 Write the number two thousand and ninety-eight in figures.

14 Round 416 to the nearest ten.

Measurement

15 1m – 31cm =

16 Find the perimeter of a rectangle with sides of 3cm and 5cm.

5cm

3cm

Time

17 What is the ninth month of the year?

18 My sister gets up at twenty past seven in the morning. Show the time in digital format.

Number problems

19 What number is halfway between 57 and 63?

20 What number is 100 more than 499?

Score chart

Test	6	7	8	9	10	Progress
Score						

TEST 11

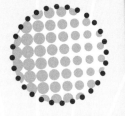

Brodie's Brain Booster

One piece of wood is 50cm long and another piece is 1¼ metres long. If I join the two pieces end to end, what is the total length in centimetres?

1 Write the number nine thousand and two in figures.

2 What number is halfway between 89 and 95?

3 Put these numbers in order, starting with the smallest:
878 8 788 78 87 887

4 Round 825 to the nearest ten.

5 What number is 100 more than 176?

6 What is the next number in this sequence? 48, 52, 56, 60, …

7 I think of a number. I add 31. My answer is 50. What number did I first think of?

8 What is my change from £1 when I spend 72p?

9 16p + 22p =

10 Multiply 3 by 9.

11 Double 12 =

12 8 x 6 =

13 What is 7 multiplied by 9?

14 What fraction of the circle is shaded?

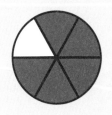

15 Simplify the fraction $\frac{8}{10}$

16 Write this fraction as a decimal $\frac{7}{10}$

17 What is the tenth month of the year?

18 Find the perimeter of a rectangle with sides of 2cm and 5cm.

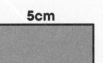

5cm

2cm

19 I finish breakfast at a quarter to eight in the morning. Show the time in digital format.

20 53cm + 17cm =

TEST 12

Digit says...
My tail is 18cm longer than the cat's. I don't like to boast but that means mine is 180mm longer!

1 Write the number four thousand and one in figures.

2 What number is halfway between 40 and 60?

3 Put these numbers in order, starting with the smallest:
249 942 924 94 294 429

4 Round 115 to the nearest ten.

5 What number is 100 more than 359?

6 What is the next number in this sequence? 37, 43, 49, 55, …

7 I think of a number. I add 53. My answer is 60. What number did I first think of?

8 What is my change from £1 when I spend 92p?

9 13p + 14p =

10 Multiply 6 by 9

11 How much do I spend when I buy 4 pencils costing 48p each?

12 Double 13 =

13 9 x 7 =

14 What fraction of the circle is shaded?

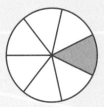

15 Simplify the fraction $\frac{3}{9}$

16 Write this fraction as a decimal $\frac{8}{10}$

17 What is the eleventh month of the year?

18 Find the perimeter of a rectangle with sides of 1cm and 6cm.
6cm   1cm

19 I am always dressed by twenty-five past seven in the morning. Show the time in digital format.

20 65cm + 15cm =

Score: 20

1 Write the number ten thousand in figures.

10000

2 What number is halfway between 20 and 40?

30

3 Put these numbers in order, starting with the smallest:
567 765 675 657 756 576

567 576 657 675 756 765

4 Round 381 to the nearest hundred.

400

5 What number is 100 more than 900?

1000

6 What is the next number in this sequence? 45, 54, 63, 72, …

81

7 I think of a number. I add 24. My answer is 80. What number did I first think of?

56

8 What is my change from £1 when I spend 89p?

11p

9 11p + 15p = 26p

10 What is 8 multiplied by 6? 42

11 Multiply 7 by 7. 49

12 How much do I spend when I buy 4 pencils costing 53p each?

212p

13 Double 14 = 28

14 What fraction of the circle is shaded?

$\frac{2}{7}$

15 Simplify the fraction $\frac{6}{9}$ $\frac{2}{3}$

16 Write this fraction as a decimal $\frac{9}{10}$

0.9

17 What is the twelfth month of the year?

December

18 Find the perimeter of a rectangle with sides of 1cm and 5cm.

5cm

1cm

12cm

19 I arrive at school at half past eight in the morning. Show the time in digital format.

8.30 am

20 77cm + 13cm = 90cm

Brodie's Brain Booster

Digit and I went for an 8km walk. I stopped for a rest after 4½ km. How much further did we have to go?

TEST 14

Score:

1 Write the number thirteen thousand in figures.

2 What number is halfway between 20 and 60?

3 Put these numbers in order, starting with the smallest: 1,450 26 1,000 654 1,026 462

4 Round 456 to the nearest hundred.

5 What number is 100 more than 954?

6 What is the next number in this sequence? 36, 44, 52, 60, …

7 I think of a number. I add 35. My answer is 90. What number did I first think of?

8 What is my change from £1 when I spend 26p?

9 13p + 12p =

10 7 x 6 =

11 What is 8 multiplied by 3?

12 Multiply 3 by 9.

13 How much do I spend when I buy 5 pencils costing 49p each?

14 What fraction of the circle is shaded?

15 Simplify the fraction $\frac{6}{8}$

16 Write this fraction as a decimal $\frac{1}{10}$

17 What is the first month of the year?

18 Find the perimeter of a rectangle with sides of 2cm and 4cm.

4cm

2cm

19 My school starts at five minutes to nine in the morning. Show the time in digital format.

20 62cm + 18cm =

Digit says...

My dog food costs £12.99 for one bag but the cat's food is £1.30 cheaper. I'm definitely worth it!

Digit's dog food costs £12.99 but the cat food is £1.30 cheaper. How much does the cat food cost?

1 Write the number seventeen thousand in figures.

2 What number is halfway between 20 and 80?

3 Put these numbers in order, starting with the smallest:
2,500 1,250 5,000 2,750 3,250 1,500

4 Round 381 to the nearest hundred.

5 What number is 100 more than 929?

6 What is the next number in this sequence? 20, 29, 38, 47, …

7 I think of a number. I add 14. My answer is 80. What number did I first think of?

8 What is my change from £1 when I spend 56p?

9 18p + 50p =

10 Double 15 =

11 5 x 7 =

12 What is 9 multiplied by 8?

13 Multiply 4 by 11.

14 What fraction of the circle is shaded?

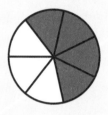

15 Simplify the fraction $\frac{2}{8}$

16 Write this fraction as a decimal $\frac{2}{10}$

17 What is the second month of the year?

18 Find the perimeter of a rectangle with sides of 3cm and 4cm.

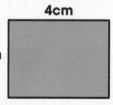

19 My school assembly starts at ten minutes to ten in the morning. Show the time in digital format.

20 36cm + 14cm =

Progress Test 3

Addition

1 46 + 23 =

2 What is the total of 32p and 47p?

Subtraction

3 60 − 35 =

4 94 take away 19 =

Multiplication

5 How much do I spend when I buy 5 pencils costing 58p each?

6 Double 16 =

Division

7 16 ÷ 2 =

8 Share 9 sweets between 3 people.

Money

9 What is my change from £1 when I spend 44p?

10 36p + 66p =

Fractions

11 What fraction of the circle is shaded?

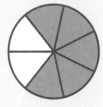

12 Simplify the fraction $\frac{4}{8}$

Number knowledge

13 Write the number nineteen thousand in figures.

14 Round 385 to the nearest ten.

Measurement

15 Find the perimeter of a rectangle with sides of 2cm and 7cm.

2cm **7cm**

16 75cm + 15cm =

Time

17 My school breaktime starts at twenty-five minutes to eleven in the morning. Show the time in digital format.

18 What is the ninth month of the year?

Number problems

19 What number is halfway between 20 and 50?

20 I think of a number. I add 84. My answer is 100. What number did I think of?

Score chart

Test	11	12	13	14	15	Progress
Score						

20

Score:

1 Write the number two hundred and forty-nine in figures.

2 88 + 72 =

3 How many days are there in one year (not a leap year)?

4 Which of these is a prime number?
6 7 8 9 10

5 Put these numbers in order, starting with the smallest:
247 742 274 427 724 472

6 Add 56 to 38.

7 Round 381 to the nearest ten.

8 What number is 100 less than 267?

9 What is the next number in this sequence: 27, 29, 31, 33, ...

10 How much do I spend when I buy 4 pencils costing 67p each?

11 I think of a number. I add 14. My answer is 31. What number did I first think of?

12 What fraction of the circle is shaded?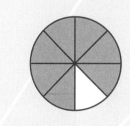

13 What is my change from £1 when I spend 72p?

14 65p + 42p + 39p =

15 Simplify the fraction $\frac{6}{8}$

16 28 ÷ 7 =

17 Write this fraction as a decimal $\frac{1}{4}$

18 How many metres are there in half a kilometre?

19 Find the perimeter of a rectangle with sides of 4cm and 6cm.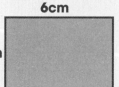

6cm
4cm

20 I get up at quarter past seven in the morning. Show the time in digital format.

Digit says...

Remember that there are 60 minutes in one hour so there must be 30 minutes in half an hour.

Score:

1 How many days are there in July?

2 Add 300 to 145.

3 17 + 18 + 19 =

4 What is my change from £1 when I spend 48p?

5 Look at the time on the digital clock. What time will it be ten minutes later?

6 Round 427 to the nearest ten.

7 9 x 7 =

8 What number is 100 more than 832?

9 Write the correct number in the box.

6 + 4 = 7 +

10 Write the correct number in the box.

4 x [ ] = 32

11 Write this fraction as a decimal $\frac{3}{4}$

12 What fraction of the rectangle is shaded?

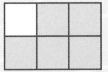

13 Write the next number in this sequence: 42, 47, 52, 57, …

14 45 ÷ 9 =

15 How many minutes are there in half an hour?

16 I think of a number. I add 7. My answer is 102. What number did I first think of?

17 1 – 0.6 =

18 £1.43 + £1.17 =

19 Find the perimeter of a rectangle with sides of 3cm and 5cm.

5cm

3cm

20 Write the number six hundred and thirty-two in figures.

Brodie's Brain Booster

A bag of Digit's dog food costs £12.99. If I buy 1 bag, how much change would I have from £20?

Score:

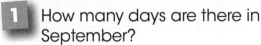

1 How many days are there in September?

2 This is the time I get home in the evening. Show the time in digital format.

Digit says...
Yesterday's walk lasted for an hour and a half so that was 90 minutes altogether! Time for a nap...

3 I think of a number. I add 20. My answer is 106. What number did I first think of?

11 Write this fraction as a decimal $\frac{6}{10}$

12 $1 - 0.7 =$

13 Write the next number in this sequence: 38, 42, 46, 50, …

4 What is my change from £1 when I spend 16p?

14 $72 \div 8 =$

15 How many metres are there in a quarter of a kilometre?

5 Round 689 to the nearest ten.

16 What fraction of the square is shaded?

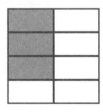

6 Write the number four hundred and seven in figures.

17 $51 - 27 =$

7 $6 \times 8 =$

18 £2.72 + £1.08 =

8 Multiply forty-six by ten.

19 Find the perimeter of a rectangle with sides of 2cm and 8cm.

8cm
2cm

9 Write the correct number in the box.

$8 + 5 = 9 +$ ☐

10 Write the correct number in the box.

$7 \times$ ☐ $= 63$

20 What number is 100 more than 216?

TEST 19

Brodie's Brain Booster

A bag of Digit's dog food costs £12.99. What would 2 bags cost?

1 How many days are there in March?

2 This is the time I have lunch. Show the time in digital format.

3 1 – 0.4 =

4 42 ÷ 6 =

5 Find the perimeter of a rectangle with sides of 3cm and 6cm

6cm

3cm

6 13 + 14 + 15 =

7 How many metres are there in three quarters of a kilometre?

8 I think of a number. I add 15. My answer is 63. What number did I first think of?

9 Write the correct number in the box:

9 + 8 = [ ] + 6

10 Write the correct number in the box:

4 x [ ] = 36

11 Write this fraction as a decimal $\frac{9}{10}$

12 I think of a number. I add 15. My answer is 101. What number did I first think of?

13 Write the next number in this sequence: 19, 22, 25, 28, …

14 What is my change from £1 when I spend 39p?

15 5 x 9 =

16 What fraction of the circle is shaded?

17 Write the number nine hundred and two in figures.

18 £5.46 + £2.50 =

19 Round 703 to the nearest ten.

20 What number is 100 more than 984?

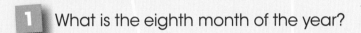

TEST 20

Score:

1 What is the eighth month of the year?

2 Write the number four hundred and ninety-nine in figures.

3 How many metres are there in one tenth of a kilometre?

4 Subtract 63 from 88.

5 Find the perimeter of a square with sides of 9cm.

9cm

9cm

6 8 x 8 =

7 Write the next number in this sequence: 15, 22, 29, 36, …

8 £4.26 + £3.17 =

9 Write this fraction as a decimal $\frac{7}{10}$

10 54p + 32p =

11 How many minutes are there in a quarter of an hour?

12 I think of a number. I add 16. My answer is 42. What number did I first think of?

13 54 ÷ 9 =

14 What is my change from £1 when I spend 68p?

15 Multiply thirty-seven by ten.

16 How many metres are there in three tenths of a kilometre?

17 Simplify the fraction $\frac{2}{8}$

18 How many days are there in a fortnight?

19 Write these numbers in order, starting with the smallest: 612 261 216 621 162 126

20 1 – 0.2 =

Digit says...

Did you know that a heptagon is a shape with seven sides?

Addition

1 67 + 49 =

2 17 + 18 + 19 =

Subtraction

3 62 – 38 =

4 100 – 56 =

Multiplication

5 7 x 6 =

6 42 x 10 =

Division

7 32 ÷ 4 =

8 60 ÷ 10 =

Money

9 What is my change from £1 when I spend 38p?

10 54p + 37p =

Fractions

11 Simplify the fraction $\frac{4}{8}$

12 Write the fraction seven tenths as a decimal.

Number knowledge

13 Write the number five hundred and eight in figures.

14 Round the number 317 to the nearest ten.

Measurement

15 How many centimetres are there in a quarter of a metre?

16 What is the perimeter of a rectangle of sides 3cm and 7cm?

7cm

3cm

Time

17 I have breakfast at a quarter to eight. Write this time in digital format.

18 How many minutes are there in half an hour?

Number problems

19 I think of a number. I add 8. My answer is 33. What number did I first think of?

20 I think of a number. I add 16. My answer is 51. What number did I first think of?

Score chart

Test	16	17	18	19	20	Progress
Score						

TEST 21

Brodie's Brain Booster

It's Digit's birthday and he is 3 years old. How many months is that?

1. 45 + 23 + 6 =

2. What number is halfway between 40 and 70?

3. Put these numbers in order, starting with the smallest:
4,200 2,400 4,020 4,002 2,004 2,040

4. Round 932 to the nearest hundred.

5. What number is 1,000 less than 2,670?

6. What is the next number in this sequence? 45, 48, 51, 54, ...

7. I think of a number. I add 49. My answer is 90. What number did I first think of?

8. What is my change from £1 when I spend 39p?

9. 14p + 61p =

10. 8 x 7 =

11. What is 4 multiplied by 12?

12. Multiply 9 by 9.

13. How much do I spend when I buy 5 pencils costing 99p each?

14. What fraction of the circle is shaded?

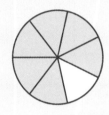

15. Simplify the fraction $\frac{3}{6}$

16. Write this fraction as a decimal $\frac{3}{10}$

17. How many days are there in January?

18. Find the perimeter of a rectangle with sides of 3cm and 7cm.

7cm

3cm

19. Lunchtime starts at a quarter past twelve in the afternoon. Show the time in digital format.

20. 1m – 17cm =

27

TEST 22

Digit says...

Sometimes on my walk I go towards north-east and then I run in the opposite direction, which is south-west.

1 38 + 21 + 17 =

2 What number is halfway between 50 and 80?

3 Put these numbers in order, starting with the smallest:
500 5,000 250 750 1,500 5,100

4 Round 489 to the nearest hundred.

5 What number is 1,000 less than 4,319?

6 What is the next number in this sequence? 92, 94, 96, 98, …

7 I think of a number. I add 28. My answer is 70. What number did I first think of?

8 What is my change from £1 when I spend 18p?

9 16p + 15p =

10 Double 17 =

11 9 x 7 =

12 What is 8 multiplied by 6?

13 Multiply 6 by 11.

14 What fraction of the circle is shaded?

15 Simplify the fraction $\frac{2}{6}$

16 Write this fraction as a decimal $\frac{4}{10}$

17 How many days are there in February (not in a leap year)?

18 Find the perimeter of a rectangle with sides of 4cm and 7cm.

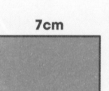

7cm

4cm

19 I go out to break at about twenty past twelve in the afternoon. Show the time in digital format.

20 1m – 62cm =

TEST 23

Score:

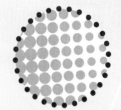

1. 29 + 17 + 14 =

2. What number is halfway between 70 and 100?

3. Put these numbers in order, starting with the smallest: 7,500 750 500 2,500 5,000 250

4. Round 306 to the nearest hundred.

5. What number is 1,000 less than 8,014?

6. What is the next number in this sequence? 89, 92, 95, 98, …

7. I think of a number. I add 35. My answer is 71. What number did I think of?

8. What is my change from £1 when I spend 61p?

9. 11p + 23p =

10. How much do I spend when I buy 5 pencils costing 84p each?

11. Double 18 =

12. 12 x 4 =

13. What is 9 multiplied by 6?

14. What fraction of the circle is shaded?

15. Simplify the fraction $\frac{4}{6}$

16. Write this fraction as a decimal $\frac{5}{10}$

17. How many days are there in February in a leap year?

18. Find the perimeter of a rectangle with sides of 5cm and 7cm.

7cm

5cm

19. I go in for lunch at about twenty-five past twelve in the afternoon. Show the time in digital format.

20. 1m - 44cm.

Brodie's Brain Booster

It's Sam's ninth birthday today. How many months old is Sam?

29

Score:

1 32 + 21 + 13 =

2 What number is halfway between 50 and 100?

3 Put these numbers in order, starting with the smallest:
2,000 6,000 5,000 4,000 3,000 7,000

4 Round 995 to the nearest hundred.

5 What number is 1,000 less than 6,254?

6 What is the next number in this sequence? 86, 90, 94, 98, …

7 I think of a number. I add 46. My answer is 81. What number did I think of?

8 What is my change from £1 when I spend 48p?

9 17p + 14p =

10 Multiply 8 by 11.

11 How much do I spend when I buy 5 pencils costing 62p each?

12 Double 19 =

13 3 x 12 =

14 What fraction of the circle is shaded?

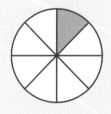

15 Simplify the fraction $\frac{2}{4}$

16 Write this fraction as a decimal $\frac{6}{10}$

17 How many days are there in March?

18 Find the perimeter of a rectangle with sides of 6cm and 7cm.

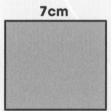

7cm

6cm

19 I start my lunch at about half past twelve in the afternoon. Show the time in digital format.

20 1m – 83cm =

Digit says...

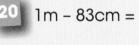

Sometimes on my walk I go towards south-east then I run in the opposite direction, which is north-west.

Score:

1 17 + 18 + 19 =

2 What number is halfway between 90 and 100?

3 Put these numbers in order, starting with the smallest:
4,250 7,750 4,750 6,250 2,250 5,500

4 Round 112 to the nearest hundred.

5 What number is 1,000 less than 5,067?

6 What is the next number in this sequence? 84, 89, 94, 99, …

7 I think of a number.
I add 62. My answer is 95.
What number did I first think of?

8 What is my change from £1 when I spend 85p?

9 30p + 18p =

10 What is 6 multiplied by 11?

11 Multiply 12 by 4.

12 How much do I spend when I buy 5 pencils costing 75p each?

13 Double 21 =

14 What fraction of the circle is shaded?

15 Simplify the fraction $\frac{2}{10}$

16 Write this fraction as a decimal $\frac{7}{10}$

17 How many days are there in April?

18 Find the perimeter of a square with sides of 6cm.

6cm

6cm

19 I finish my lunch at about twenty to one in the afternoon. Show the time in digital format.

20 1m – 13cm =

Addition

1 26 + 27 + 28 =

2 87 + 73 =

Subtraction

3 What number is 1,000 less than 5,614?

4 100 – 52 =

Multiplication

5 Multiply 8 by 12.

6 Double 27 =

Division

7 56 ÷ 7 =

8 100 ÷ 4 =

Money

9 62p + 28p =

10 How much do I spend when I buy 5 pencils costing 35p each?

Fractions

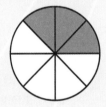

11 What fraction of the circle is shaded?

12 Write this fraction as a decimal $\frac{8}{10}$

Number knowledge

13 Put these numbers in order, starting with the smallest:
6,117 711 671 761 1,176 7,611

14 Round 365 to the nearest hundred.

Measurement

15 1m – 59cm =

16 Find the perimeter of a square with sides of 2cm.

2cm

2cm

Time

17 I go out to break at about a quarter to one in the afternoon. Show the time in digital format.

16 How many days are there in May?

Number problems

19 What number is halfway between 60 and 90?

20 I think of a number. I add 37. My answer is 84. What number did I first think of?

Test	21	22	23	24	25	Progress
Score						

Score chart

32

TEST 26

Score:

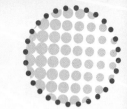

1 47 + 43 + 20 =

2 What number is halfway between 100 and 200?

3 Put these numbers in order, starting with the smallest:
1,600 2,500 8,700 4,900 2,300 1,800

4 Round 697 to the nearest thousand.

5 What number is 1,000 less than 10,000?

6 What is the next number in this sequence? 41, 36, 31, 26, …

7 I think of a number. I subtract 56. My answer is 92. What number did I first think of?

8 What is my change from £1 when I spend 14p?

9 32p + 12p =

10 28 ÷ 7 =

11 Half of 16 =

12 What is 32 shared between 4?

13 What is the product of 6 and 8?

14 What fraction of the circle is shaded?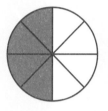

15 Simplify the fraction $\frac{4}{10}$

16 Write this fraction as a decimal $\frac{9}{10}$

17 How many days are there in June?

18 Find the perimeter of a square with sides of 3cm.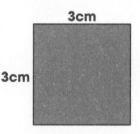

3cm

3cm

19 How many minutes are there in half an hour?

20 76cm + 24cm =

Digit says...

Yesterday's walk lasted for an hour and a half and we set out at 11am so we got back at 12.30pm. Just in time for lunch!

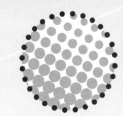

1 60 + 70 + 80 =

2 What number is halfway between 100 and 120?

3 Put these numbers in order, starting with the smallest:
3.6 4.2 5.9 1.7 2.6 6.1

4 Round 2,381 to the nearest thousand.

5 What number is 1,000 less than 10,145?

6 What is the next number in this sequence? 27, 24, 21, 18, ...

7 I think of a number. I subtract 14. My answer is 46. What number did I think of?

8 What is my change from £1 when I spend 23p?

9 23p + 37p =

10 Which of these is a prime number?
6 7 8 9 10

11 48 ÷ 6 =

12 Half of 12 =

13 What is 20 shared between 4?

14 What fraction of the circle is shaded?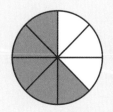

15 Simplify the fraction $\frac{6}{10}$

16 Write this fraction as a decimal $\frac{1}{100}$

17 How many days are there in July?

18 Find the perimeter of a square with sides of 4cm.

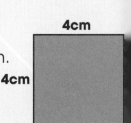
4cm
4cm

19 How many minutes are there in a quarter of an hour?

20 32cm + 38cm =

Brodie's Brain Booster

If Digit goes for a 90 minute walk starting at 11.45am, what time will he get home?

TEST 28

Score:

1 40 + 50 + 60 =

2 What number is halfway between 100 and 140?

3 Put these numbers in order, starting with the smallest:
5.8 9.4 1.9 6.7 2.4 3.1

4 Round 4,725 to the nearest thousand.

5 What number is 1,000 more than 2,267?

6 What is the next number in this sequence? 29, 22, 15, 8, …

7 I think of a number. I subtract 23. My answer is 77. What number did I first think of?

8 What is my change from £1 when I spend 35p?

9 19p + 34p =

10 What is the product of 7 and 2?

Digit says...

There are 100 dog biscuits in a box so in 10 boxes there will be 1000 biscuits altogether. Yummy, yummy!

11 Which of these is a prime number?
3 4 6 8 12

12 32 ÷ 4 =

13 Half of 14 =

14 What fraction of the circle is shaded?

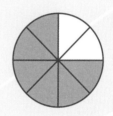

15 Simplify the fraction $\frac{8}{10}$

16 Write this fraction as a decimal $\frac{7}{100}$

17 How many days are there in August?

18 Find the perimeter of a square with sides of 5cm.

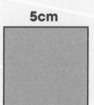

5cm

5cm

19 How many minutes are there in three quarters of an hour?

20 28cm + 42cm =

TEST 29

Score:

1 $70 + 80 + 90 =$

2 What number is halfway between 100 and 150?

3 Put these numbers in order, starting with the smallest: 8 1.8 6 2.6 5 3.5

4 Round 8,619 to the nearest thousand.

5 What number is 1,000 more than 4,387?

6 What is the next number in this sequence? 64, 56, 48, 40, …

7 I think of a number. I subtract 59. My answer is 21. What number did I first think of?

8 What is my change from £1 when I spend 46p?

9 $52p + 45p =$

10 What is 48 shared between 4?

11 What is the product of 9 and 7?

12 Which of these is a prime number? 12 13 14 15 16

13 $24 \div 6 =$

14 What fraction of the circle is shaded?

15 Simplify the fraction $\frac{3}{9}$

16 Write this fraction as a decimal $\frac{9}{100}$

17 How many days are there in September?

18 Find the perimeter of a square with sides of 7cm.

7cm

7cm

19 How many minutes are there in two hours?

20 $39cm + 41cm =$

Score:

1 30 + 80 + 90 =

2 What number is halfway between 150 and 200?

3 Put these numbers in order, starting with the smallest: 17 1.7 7.1 25 2.5 5.2

4 Round 3,555 to the nearest thousand.

5 What number is 1,000 more than 8,617?

6 What is the next number in this sequence? 72, 63, 54, 45, ...

7 I think of a number. I subtract 37. My answer is 23. What number did I first think of?

8 What is my change from £1 when I spend 57p?

9 80p + 70p =

10 Half of 18 =

11 What is 36 shared between 4?

12 What is the product of 5 and 9?

13 Which of these is a prime number? 14 15 16 17 18

14 Simplify the fraction $\frac{6}{9}$

15 What fraction of the circle is shaded?

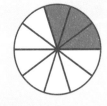

16 Write this fraction as a decimal $\frac{13}{100}$

17 How many days are there in October?

18 Find the perimeter of a square with sides of 8cm.

8cm

8cm

19 How many minutes are there in three hours?

20 46cm + 44cm =

Digit says...

Did you know that a thousand thousands make a million. I'm just imagining a pile of 1,000,000 dog biscuits!

Addition

1 40 + 60 + 80 =

2 97 + 76 =

Subtraction

3 100 – 33 =

4 101 minus 38 =

Multiplication

5 12 x 5 =

6 What is 2 multiplied by 12?

Division

7 Half of 34 =

8 54 ÷ 9 =

Money

9 What is my change from £1 when I spend 33p?

10 47p + 68p =

Fractions

11 Simplify the fraction $\frac{6}{9}$

12 Write this fraction as a decimal $\frac{27}{100}$

Number knowledge

13 Put these numbers in order, starting with the smallest: 801 18 180 8.1 1.8 108

14 What number is 1,000 more than 6,275?

Measurement

15 Find the perimeter of a square with sides of 9cm.

9cm

9cm

16 63cm + 27cm =

Time

17 How many days are there in November?

18 How many minutes are there in two hours?

Number problems

19 What number is halfway between 200 and 300?

20 I think of a number. I subtract 18. My answer is 42. What number did I first think of?

Score chart

Test	26	27	28	29	30	Progress
Score						

TEST 31

Score:

Brodie's Brain Booster

I run for $\frac{1}{4}$km then stop for a drink. How many metres have I run before having my drink?

1. 110 + 120 =

2. What number is halfway between 0 and 500?

3. Put these numbers in order, starting with the smallest:
   6.5 89 56 5.6 9.8 8.9

4. Round 1,848 to the nearest thousand

5. What number is 1,000 more than 3,986?

6. What is the next number in this sequence? 49, 42, 35, 28, …

7. I think of a number. I subtract 92. My answer is 80. What number did I first think of?

8. What is my change from £1 when I spend 68p?

9. 68p + 67p =

10. 42 ÷ 7 =

11. Half of 22 =

12. What is 40 shared between 5?

13. What is the product of 4 and 8?

14. What fraction of the circle is shaded?

15. Simplify the fraction $\frac{4}{8}$

16. Write this fraction as a decimal $\frac{39}{100}$

17. What is the third month of the year?

18. Find the perimeter of a square with sides of 6cm.

6cm

6cm

19. Lunchtime finishes at five past one in the afternoon. Write this time in digital form.

20. 1m − 12cm =

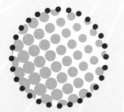

Score:

Digit says...

Remember there are 1000 millilitres in a litre.

1 120 + 140 =

2 What number is halfway between 300 and 400?

3 Put these numbers in order, starting with the smallest:
30 0.3 3.0 40 0.4 4.0

4 Round 5,001 to the nearest thousand.

5 What number is 1,000 more than 653?

6 What is the next number in this sequence? 81, 75, 69, 63, ...

7 I think of a number. I subtract 29. My answer is 61. What number did I first think of?

8 What is my change from £1 when I spend 79p?

9 72p + 78p =

10 Which of these is a prime number?
20 21 22 23 24

11 36 ÷ 9 =

12 Half of 24 =

13 What is 48 shared between 6?

14 What fraction of the circle is shaded?

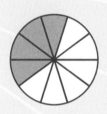

15 Simplify the fraction $\frac{5}{10}$

16 Write this fraction as a decimal $\frac{46}{100}$

17 What is the fourth month of the year?

18 Find the perimeter of a square with sides of 10cm.

10cm

10cm

19 School finishes at a quarter past three in the afternoon. Show the time in digital format.

20 1m - 18cm =

Score:

1 150 + 130 =

2 What number is halfway between 0 and 1,000?

3 Put these numbers in order, starting with the smallest: 5.0 50 0.5 2.5 5.2 0.2

4 Round 7,325 to the nearest thousand.

5 What number is 1,000 more than 9,246?

6 What is the next number in this sequence? 81, 74, 67, 60, …

7 I think of a number. I subtract 42. My answer is 58. What number did I first think of?

8 What is my change from £1 when I spend 81p?

9 84p + 89p =

10 What is the product of 7 and 5?

11 Which of these is a prime number? 25 26 27 28 29

12 36 ÷ 6 =

13 Half of 26 =

14 What fraction of the circle is shaded?

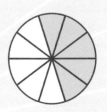

15 Simplify the fraction $\frac{2}{4}$

16 Write this fraction as a decimal $\frac{51}{100}$

17 What is the fifth month of the year?

18 Find the perimeter of a square with sides of 11cm.

11cm

11cm

19 I get home from school at about half past three in the afternoon. Show the time in digital format.

20 1m – 23cm =

Brodie's Brain Booster

I run for $\frac{3}{4}$km and then have a drink. How many metres is this?

41

Score:

1 180 + 120 =

2 What number is halfway between 200 and 500?

3 Put these numbers in order, starting with the smallest:
46 4.6 27 7.2 6.4 2.7

4 Round 6,499 to the nearest thousand.

5 What number is 1,000 more than 9,999?

6 What is the next number in this sequence? 100, 91, 82, 73, …

7 I think of a number. I subtract 61. My answer is 18. What number did I first think of?

8 What is my change from £1 when I spend 92p?

9 95p + 24p =

10 What is 63 shared between 9?

11 What is the product of 7 and 8?

12 Which of these is a prime number?
31 32 33 34 35

13 72 ÷ 8 =

14 What fraction of the circle is shaded?

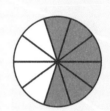

15 Simplify the fraction $\frac{6}{8}$

16 Write this fraction as a decimal $\frac{62}{100}$

17 What is the sixth month of the year?

18 Find the perimeter of a square with sides of 12cm.

12cm

12cm

19 I have a snack at about 4 o'clock in the afternoon. Show the time in digital format.

20 1m – 42cm =

Digit says…

I drank $1\frac{3}{4}$L of water, which is 1750ml. I need to go outside…

TEST 35

Score:

Brodie's Brain Booster

Digit runs for $\frac{1}{8}$km then sits down to wait for me. How many metres is $\frac{1}{8}$km?

1 170 + 150 =

2 What number is halfway between 300 and 600?

3 Put these numbers in order, starting with the smallest:
240 4.2 402 204 2.4 420

4 Round 2,501 to the nearest thousand.

5 What number is 1,000 more than 9,750?

6 What is the next number in this sequence? 100, 92, 84, 76, …

7 I think of a number. I subtract 77. My answer is 23. What number did I first think of?

8 What is my change from £1 when I spend 13p?

9 14p + 88p =

10 Half of 28 =

11 What is 72 shared between 8?

12 What is the product of 9 and 6?

13 Which of these is a prime number?
4 6 7 9 12

14 What fraction of the circle is shaded?

15 Simplify the fraction $\frac{2}{6}$

16 Write this fraction as a decimal $\frac{74}{100}$

17 What is the seventh month of the year?

18 Find the perimeter of a square with sides of 13cm.

13cm

13cm

19 I start watching television at about ten past five in the afternoon. Show the time in digital format.

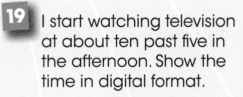

20 1m – 68cm =

43

Addition

1 180 + 140 =

2 What number is 100 more than 799?

Subtraction

3 What number is 100 less than 128?

4 1,000 – 750 =

Multiplication

5 How much do I spend when I buy 5 pencils costing 35p each?

6 12 x 7 =

Money

7 What is 48 shared between 12?

8 Half of 30 =

Division

9 What is my change from £1 when I spend 55p?

10 44p + 79p =

Fractions

11 Write this fraction as a decimal $\frac{85}{100}$

12 Simplify the fraction $\frac{4}{6}$

Number knowledge

13 Write the number six thousand, two hundred and forty-nine.

14 Round 9,999 to the nearest thousand.

Measurement

15 1m – 72cm =

16 Find the perimeter of a square with sides of 14cm.

14cm

14cm

Time

17 What is the eighth month of the year?

16 I go outside to play at about a quarter past four in the afternoon. Show the time in digital format.

Number problems

19 What number is halfway between 0 and 1,500?

20 I think of a number. I subtract 25. My answer is 75. What number did I first think of?

Score chart

Test	31	32	33	34	35	Progress
Score						

ANSWERS

	Test 1	Test 2	Test 3	Test 4	Test 5	Progress Test 1
1	117	804	257	902	111	58
2	18	8	25	35	17	120
3	36 63 306 360 603 630	15 51 105 150 501 510	21 61 126 216 612 621	48 84 408 480 804 840	69 79 97 679 697 796	44
4	390	250	590	860	340	56
5	245	498	524	639	455	12
6	53	44	48	41	75	40
7	47	55	15	24	34	6
8	73	83	90	87	80p	5
9	100	34	62	40	54	75p
10	4	14	20	24	21	71p
11	24	10	72p	24	36	$\frac{2}{5}$
12	28	15	6	£1.96	35	0.5
13	88p	12	45	8	£1.25	999
14	$\frac{1}{4}$	$\frac{3}{4}$	$\frac{7}{8}$	$\frac{1}{2}$	$\frac{1}{5}$	158 185 518 581 815 851
15	$\frac{1}{2}$	$\frac{1}{4}$	$\frac{3}{4}$	$\frac{1}{2}$	$\frac{1}{3}$	60cm
16	0.5	0.25	0.75	0.25	0.75	3000
17	365	12	366	January	February	60
18	1000	500	250	750	2000	March
19	60	30	15	45	120	10
20	40cm	50cm	50cm	60cm	90cm	182

	Test 6	Test 7	Test 8	Test 9	Test 10	Progress Test 2
1	777	1,214	7,327	5,520	3,046	74
2	22	33	45	34	46	34
3	79 97 709 790 907 970	8 18 81 118 181 811	345 354 435 453 534 543	46 64 406 460 604 640	17 37 73 137 173 317	48
4	990	130	650	780	450	48
5	842	807	367	618	932	16
6	114	127	125	111	118	32
7	45	28	38	46	56	3
8	35	25	40	51	81	5
9	17	19	17	12	16	76p
10	30	36	16	£3.28	45	76p
11	27	36	20	18	£3.96	$\frac{4}{6}$ or $\frac{2}{3}$
12	£2.32	32	45	35	22	0.6
13	14	£3	18	24	36	2098
14	$\frac{3}{5}$	$\frac{4}{5}$	$\frac{1}{6}$	$\frac{2}{6}$ or $\frac{1}{3}$	$\frac{3}{6}$ or $\frac{1}{2}$	420
15	$\frac{2}{3}$	$\frac{1}{2}$	$\frac{1}{5}$	$\frac{2}{5}$	$\frac{3}{5}$	69cm
16	0.1	0.2	0.3	0.4	0.5	16cm
17	April	May	June	July	August	September
18	20cm	18cm	16cm	22cm	18cm	7.20am or 07.20
19	7.15am or 07.15	7.30am or 07.30	8am or 08.00	7am or 07.00	7.10am or 07.10	60
20	54cm	62cm	51cm	13cm	36cm	599

	Test 11	Test 12	Test 13	Test 14	Test 15	Progress Test 3
1	9,002	4,001	10,000	13,000	17,000	69
2	92	50	30	40	50	79p
3	8 78 87 788 878 887	94 249 294 429 924 942	567 576 657 675 756 765	26 462 654 1,000 1,026 1,450	1,250 1,500 2,500 2,750 3,250 5,000	25
4	830	120	400	500	400	75
5	276	459	1,000	1,054	1,029	£2.90
6	64	61	81	68	56	32
7	19	7	56	55	66	8
8	28p	8p	11p	74p	44p	3
9	38p	27p	26p	25p	68p	56p
10	27	54	48	42	30	£1.02
11	24	£1.92	49	24	35	$\frac{5}{7}$
12	48	26	£2.12	27	72	$\frac{1}{2}$
13	63	63	28	£2.45	44	19,000
14	$\frac{5}{6}$	$\frac{1}{7}$	$\frac{2}{7}$	$\frac{3}{7}$	$\frac{4}{7}$	390
15	$\frac{4}{5}$	$\frac{1}{3}$	$\frac{2}{3}$	$\frac{3}{4}$	$\frac{1}{4}$	18cm
16	0.7	0.8	0.9	0.1	0.2	90cm
17	October	November	December	January	February	10.35am or 10.35
18	14cm	14cm	12cm	12cm	14cm	September
19	7.45am or 07.45	7.25am or 07.25	8.30am or 08.30	8.55am or 08.55	9.50am or 09.50	35
20	70cm	80cm	90cm	80cm	50cm	16

	Test 16	Test 17	Test 18	Test 19	Test 20	Progress Test 4
1	249	31	30	31	August	116
2	160	445	6.25pm or 18.25	1.10pm or 13.10	499	54
3	365	54	86	0.6	100	24
4	7	52p	84p	7	25	44
5	247 274 427 472 724 742	08.05	690	18cm	36cm	42
6	94	430	407	42	64	420
7	380	63	48	750	43	8
8	167	932	460	48	£7.43	6
9	35	3	4	11	0.7	62p
10	£2.68	8	9	9	86p	91p
11	17	0.75	0.6	0.9	15	$\frac{1}{2}$
12	$\frac{7}{8}$	$\frac{5}{6}$	0.3	86	26	0.7
13	28p	62	54	31	6	508
14	£1.46	5	9	61p	32p	320
15	$\frac{3}{4}$	30	250	45	370	25
16	4	95	$\frac{3}{8}$	$\frac{2}{3}$	300	20cm
17	0.25	0.4	24	902	$\frac{1}{4}$	7.45am or 07.45
18	500	£2.60	£3.80	£7.96	14	30
19	20cm	16cm	20cm	700	126 162 216 261 612 621	25
20	7.15am or 07.15	632	316	1,084	0.8	35

	Test 21	Test 22	Test 23	Test 24	Test 25	Progress Test 5
1	74	76	60	66	54	81
2	55	65	85	75	95	160
3	2,004 2,040 2,400 4,002 4,020 4,200	250 500 750 1,500 5,000 5,100	250 500 750 2,500 5,000 7,500	2,000 3,000 4,000 5,000 6,000 7,000	2,250 4,250 4,750 5,500 6,250 7,750	4,614
4	900	500	300	1,000	100	48
5	1,670	3,319	7,014	5,254	4,067	96
6	57	100	101	102	104	54
7	41	42	36	35	33	8
8	61p	82p	39p	52p	15p	25
9	75p	31p	34p	31p	48p	90p
10	56	34	£4.20	88	66	£1.75
11	48	63	36	£3.10	48	$\frac{3}{8}$
12	81	48	48	38	£3.75	0.8
13	£4.95	66	54	36	42	671 711 761 1,176 6,117 7,611
14	$\frac{6}{7}$	$\frac{1}{3}$	$\frac{2}{3}$	$\frac{1}{8}$	$\frac{2}{8}$ or $\frac{1}{4}$	400
15	$\frac{1}{2}$	$\frac{1}{3}$	$\frac{2}{3}$	$\frac{1}{2}$	$\frac{1}{5}$	41cm
16	0.3	0.4	0.5	0.6	0.7	8cm
17	31	28	29	31	30	12.45pm or 12.45
18	20cm	22cm	24cm	26cm	24cm	31
19	12.15pm or 12.15	12.20pm or 12.20	12.25pm or 12.25	12.30pm or 12.30	12.40pm or 12.40	75
20	83cm	38cm	56cm	17cm	87cm	47

	Test 26	Test 27	Test 28	Test 29	Test 30	Progress Test 6
1	110	210	150	240	200	180
2	150	110	120	125	175	173
3	1,600 1,800 2,300 2,500 4,900 8,700	1.7 2.6 3.6 4.2 5.9 6.1	1.9 2.4 3.1 5.8 6.7 9.4	1.8 2.6 3.5 5 6 8	1.7 2.5 5.2 7.1 17 25	67
4	1000	2,000	5,000	9,000	4,000	63
5	9,000	9,145	3,267	5,387	9,617	60
6	21	15	1	32	36	24
7	148	60	100	80	60	17
8	86p	77p	65p	54p	43p	6
9	44p	60p	53p	97p	£1.50	67p
10	4	7	14	12	9	£1.15
11	8	8	3	63	9	$\frac{2}{3}$
12	8	6	8	13	45	0.27
13	48	5	7	4	17	1.8 8.1 18 108 180 801
14	$\frac{4}{8}$ or $\frac{1}{2}$	$\frac{5}{8}$	$\frac{6}{8}$ or $\frac{3}{4}$	$\frac{1}{10}$	$\frac{2}{3}$	7,275
15	$\frac{2}{5}$	$\frac{3}{5}$	$\frac{4}{5}$	$\frac{1}{3}$	$\frac{3}{10}$	36cm
16	0.9	0.01	0.07	0.09	0.13	90cm
17	30	31	31	30	31	30
18	12cm	16cm	20cm	28cm	32cm	120
19	30	15	45	120	180	250
20	1m or 100cm	70cm	70cm	80cm	90cm	60

	Test 31	Test 32	Test 33	Test 34	Test 35	Progress Test 7
1	230	260	280	300	320	320
2	250	350	500	350	450	899
3	5.6 6.5 8.9 9.8 56 89	0.3 0.4 3.0 4.0 30 40	0.2 0.5 2.5 5.0 5.2 50	2.7 4.6 6.4 7.2 27 46	2.4 4.2 204 240 402 420	28
4	2,000	5,000	7,000	6,000	3,000	250
5	4,986	1,653	10,246	10,999	10,750	£1.75
6	21	57	53	64	68	84
7	172	90	100	79	100	4
8	32p	21p	19p	8p	87p	15
9	£1.35	£1.50	£1.73	£1.19	£1.02	45p
10	6	23	35	7	14	£1.23
11	11	4	29	56	9	0.85
12	8	12	6	31	54	$\frac{2}{3}$
13	32	8	13	9	7	6,249
14	$\frac{2}{10}$ or $\frac{1}{5}$	$\frac{4}{10}$ or $\frac{2}{5}$	$\frac{5}{10}$ or $\frac{1}{2}$	$\frac{6}{10}$ or $\frac{3}{5}$	$\frac{7}{10}$	10,000
15	$\frac{1}{2}$	$\frac{1}{2}$	$\frac{1}{2}$	$\frac{3}{4}$	$\frac{1}{3}$	28cm
16	0.39	0.46	0.51	0.62	0.74	56cm
17	March	April	May	June	July	August
18	24cm	40cm	44cm	48cm	52cm	4.15pm or 16.15
19	1.05pm or 13.05	3.15pm or 15.15	3.30pm or 15.30	4pm or 16.00	5.10pm or 17.10	750
20	88cm	82cm	77cm	58cm	32cm	100

Brodie's Brain Booster

Test 1	200
Test 3	800
Test 5	450
Test 7	25
Test 9	75
Test 11	15cm
Test 13	$3\frac{1}{2}$ km
Test 15	£11.69
Test 17	£7.01
Test 19	£25.98
Test 21	36
Test 23	108
Test 25	South-west
Test 27	1.15pm
Test 29	10,000
Test 31	250
Test 33	750
Test 35	125

Digit says...

"Well done and see you next time"